# SRA
# Open Court Reading

# Reading and Writing Workbook

## Workbook 1

### Program Authors

Marilyn Jager Adams
Carl Bereiter
Anne McKeough
Robbie Case
Marsha Roit
Jan Hirshberg
Michael Pressley
Iva Carruthers
Gerald H. Treadway, Jr.

A Division of The McGraw·Hill Companies

Columbus, Ohio

## SRA/McGraw-Hill

*A Division of The* **McGraw·Hill** *Companies*

Copyright © 2000 by SRA/McGraw-Hill.

**Send all inquiries to:**
SRA/McGraw-Hill
8787 Orion Place
Columbus, Ohio 43240-4027

Printed in the United States of America.

ISBN 0-02-831064-0

21 22 23 24 25   DBH   10 09 08 07 06

# Table *of* Contents

Directions: Write as many letters as will fit on each line of these practice pages.

A

a

B

b

# Writing Letters

Directions: Write as many letters as will fit on each line of these practice pages.

C _____

c _____

D _____

d _____

*Letter Knowledge* • **Reading and Writing Workbook**

Name _____

## Writing Letters

Directions: Write as many letters as will fit on each line of these practice pages.

# Writing Letters

Directions: Write as many letters as will fit on each line of these practice pages.

H

h

I

i

J

j

*Letter Knowledge* • **Reading and Writing Workbook**

## Writing Letters

Directions: Write as many letters as will fit on each line of these practice pages.

# Writing Letters

Directions: Write as many letters as will fit on each line of these practice pages.

N

n

O

o

P

p

*Letter Knowledge* • **Reading and Writing Workbook**

# Writing Letters

Q

q

R

r

S

s

Name ______________________________

## Writing Letters

Unit 1 • Lesson 8

Directions: Write as many letters as will fit on each line of these practice pages.

T

t

U

u

V

v

## Writing Letters

W

W

X

X

Directions: Write as many letters as will fit on each line of these practice pages.

Y _____

y _____

Z _____

z _____

## Capital and Small Letters

Directions: Connect the dots from a to z.

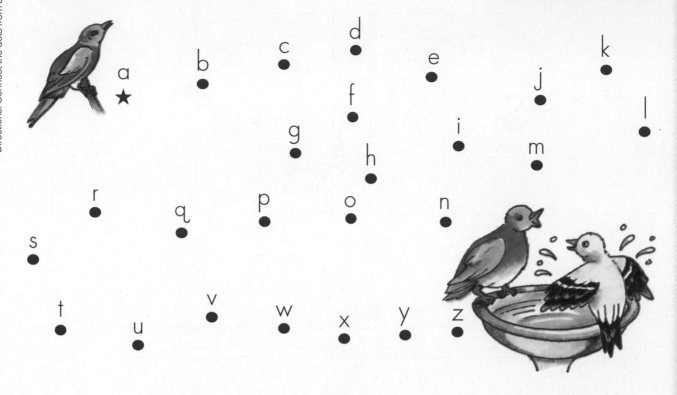

# Sounds and Spellings

s

S ‑ ‑ ‑ ‑ ‑ ‑ ‑ ‑ ‑ ‑ ‑ ‑ ‑ ‑ ‑ ‑ ‑ ‑ ‑ ‑

s ‑ ‑ ‑ ‑ ‑ ‑ ‑ ‑ ‑ ‑ ‑ ‑ ‑ ‑ ‑ ‑ ‑ ‑ ‑ ‑

## Listen for Consonants

_____    _____    _____

## Listen for Consonants

Directions: Write s next to each picture that begins with /s/.

  _____

  _____

 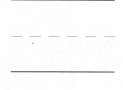 _____

  _____

 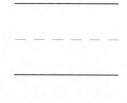 _____

  _____

 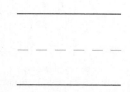 _____

 _____

Directions: Review "The House that Jack Built." Ask the children to look at these three scenes from the story. Tell them to write 1, 2, or 3 under the appropriate pictures, according to the order of events.

_____
- - - - - - - - - - - - - - - - -
_____

_____
- - - - - - - - - - - - - - - - -
_____

_____
- - - - - - - - - - - - - - - - -
_____

Name _____

# Sequence

Directions: Instruct the children to write 1, 2, or 3 under the appropriate pictures, according to the order of events.

_____

- - - - - - - - - - - - -

_____

_____

- - - - - - - - - - - - -

_____

_____

- - - - - - - - - - - - -

_____

## Sounds and Spellings

Directions: Practice writing *m* and *M*. Then write *m* under each picture that has the /m/ sound.

m

m

M

## Listening for Consonants

*Consonant Sounds and Spellings* • **Reading and Writing Workbook**

# Listening for Consonants

Directions: Write *m* in the first space if the picture starts with /m/.
Write *m* in the second space if the picture ends with /m/.

_____
- - - - - - - - - - -
_____

_____
- - - - - - - - - - -
_____

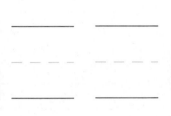

_____
- - - - - - - - - - -
_____

_____
- - - - - - - - - - -
_____

_____
- - - - - - - - - - -
_____

_____
- - - - - - - - - - -
_____

_____
- - - - - - - - - - -
_____

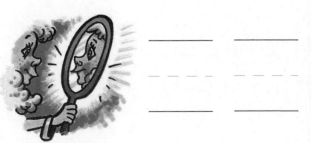

_____
- - - - - - - - - - -
_____

## Sounds and Spellings

Directions: Practice writing a and A. Then write your name in the blank in the first sentence and write a word or draw a picture to complete the second sentence.

a

a

A

I am _____

I am in a _____

*Vowel Sounds and Spellings* • **Reading and Writing Workbook**

Reading

I am in the

I am in the

I am a _____.  (leaf)

I am in the

I am on the

I am a _____.

I am on the

I am in the

I am a _____.

# Compare and Contrast

Directions: Review "Mrs. Goose's Baby." Discuss each picture and have the children circle A if the picture shows how the goose and chick are alike and D if the picture shows how they are different.

A     D

A     D

A     D

A     D

A     D

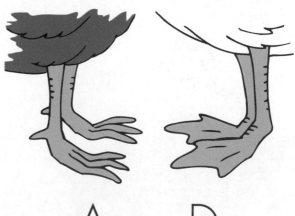

A     D

*Comprehension: Compare and Contrast* • **Reading and Writing Workbook**

Name _____

# Compare and Contrast

Directions: Continue to discuss each picture. Now have the children write A if the picture shows something that is alike and D if it shows something that is diffirent.

_____

_ _ _ _ _ _ _ _ _ _ _ _ _

_____

_____

_ _ _ _ _ _ _ _ _ _ _ _ _

_____

_____

_ _ _ _ _ _ _ _ _ _ _ _ _

_____

_____

_ _ _ _ _ _ _ _ _ _ _ _ _

_____

## Sounds and Spellings

t

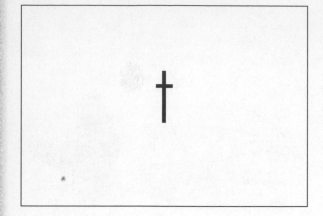

t

T

## Writing Words

at _____   mat _____

*Consonant Sounds and Spellings* • **Reading and Writing Workbook**

Name _____

## Listening for Consonants

Directions: Write *t* on the first line if the picture begins with /t/ or write *t* on the second line if the picture ends with /t/.

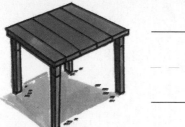
_____ _____ _____

................

_____ _____ _____

_____ _____ _____

................

_____ _____ _____

_____ _____ _____

................

_____ _____ _____

_____ _____ _____

................

_____ _____ _____

10
_____ _____ _____

................

_____ _____ _____

_____ _____ _____

................

_____ _____ _____

_____ _____ _____

................

_____ _____ _____

_____ _____ _____

................

_____ _____ _____

**Reading and Writing Workbook •** *Consonant Sounds and Spellings*

**23**

## Sounds and Spellings

Directions: Practice writing *h* and *H*. Complete the sentence by writing words for the pictures.

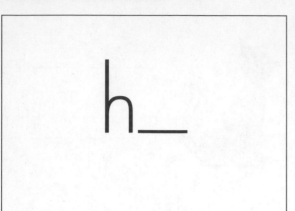

h

h

H

## Completing Sentences

A tam is a _____.

Matt has a _____.

*Consonant Sounds and Spellings* • **Reading and Writing Workbook**

# Listening for Consonants

Directions: Write *h* under each picture whose name begins with /h/.

_____

- - - - - - - - -

_____

_____

- - - - - - - - -

_____

_____

- - - - - - - - -

_____

_____

- - - - - - - - -

_____

_____

- - - - - - - - -

_____

_____

- - - - - - - - -

_____

_____

- - - - - - - - -

_____

_____

- - - - - - - - -

_____

## Sounds and Spellings

Directions: Practice writing *p* and *P*. Then copy the words and the sentence.

p

p

P

## Writing Words and Sentences

pat _____    tap _____

Pam has a map.

_____

_____

**Reading and Writing**

Pat has a hat.
Pam is at the map.

_____

_____

I tap the hat.
Pat is on a mat.

_____

_____

I tap the mat.
Pat has a hat.

_____

_____

**Reading and Writing Workbook • *Decoding***

Name _____

## Sounds and Spellings

i

i

I

## Writing Words and Sentences

him        tips

Tim sits in the pit.

*Vowel Sounds and Spellings* • **Reading and Writing Workbook**

Name _____

# Writing and Reading

Directions: Write the sound represented by each Sound/Spelling Card picture to form a word.

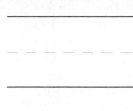

**Reading and Writing Workbook • *Blending***

## Synonyms

Directions: Have the children read the sentences, using a name for each picture. Help the children think of more than one name for each picture.

Sam has a  .

Pam is  .

Pat has a  .

The  is on the  .

*Synonyms* • **Reading and Writing Workbook**

## Synonyms

The  is in the  .

A  is on the 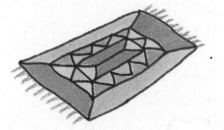 .

Sam is a  .

Tim has a  .

Directions: Have the children write each name so that it begins with a capital letter. On the last writing line, have them write their own names.

sam

_____
- - - - - - - - - - - - - -
_____

tim

_____
- - - - - - - - - - - - - -
_____

pam

_____
- - - - - - - - - - - - - -
_____

pat

_____
- - - - - - - - - - - - - -
_____

_____
- - - - - - - - - - - - - -
_____

*Capitalization* • **Reading and Writing Workbook**

**Grammar**

Directions: Have the children rewrite each sentence beginning with a capital letter.

a ham is on a mat.

_____

- - - - - - - - - - - - - - - - - - - - - -

_____

sam has a hat.

_____

- - - - - - - - - - - - - - - - - - - - - -

_____

tim sat in a pit.

_____

- - - - - - - - - - - - - - - - - - - - - -

_____

## Sounds and Spellings

Directions: Practice writing *n* and *N*. Then copy the words and the sentence.

n

n

N

## Writing Words and Sentences

# nap        man

Nan has a nap.

## Completing Sentences

_____

I nap on a _____.

ham
mat

_____

The man has a _____.

tam
tap

_____

Pam has a _____.

hat
nap

_____

Pat has a _____.

pan
map

_____

The ant is on the _____.

ham
hat

_____

Nat has a _____.

nap
pan

# Name _____

## Opposites

Directions: Have the children draw a line to match each word picture to its opposite. Column one: *short, up, happy, new;* column two: *old, sad, down, tall.*

*Opposites* • **Reading and Writing Workbook**

# Name _____

## Opposites

**Reading and Writing Workbook • *Opposites***

Name _____

# Writing Words

| pin | map | stamp | mints | ham | hat |

_____

_____

_____

_____

Directions: Look at the pictures and finish the sentences with the appropriate words.

Tim has a _____.

map
mitt

Nan sat on the _____.

hit
hat

Sam has a _____.

pin
pan

## Sounds and Spellings

d

d

D

## Writing Words and Sentences

dad _ _ _ _ _ _      mad _ _ _ _ _ _

Dad had a hat.

Directions: Practice writing d and D. Then copy the words and the sentence.

## Writing Words and Sentences

Directions: Write the word that matches each picture. Then write the sentence that matches the picture.

hat

hand  _____

_____

pan  _____

nap

map  _____

_____

Dad  _____

Dad has a pan.

Dad can nap.

Dad can pat the sand.

_____

_____

_____

# Grammar

Directions: Have the children read the words; then have them draw a line from each word to its plural.

  pin                    hats

  hat                    mitts

  mitt                   mints

  mint                   pins

*Regular Plurals* • **Reading and Writing Workbook**

## Grammar

Directions: Have the children look at each picture and read the word pair. Have them circle the word that tells about the picture; then have them write the words on the lines.

1. stamp    stamps    _____

2. hat    hats    _____

3. hand    hands    _____

4. pan    pans    _____

Name _____

## Sounds and Spellings

## Writing Words and Sentences

Dot can stop the top.

*Vowel Sounds and Spellings* • **Reading and Writing Workbook**

Directions: Finish the sentences with the appropriate word.

Dad can spin a _____ .

tap
tip
top

Pam and Sam _____ Spot.

pat
pit
pot

The pot is _____ .

hat
hit
hot

**Main idea:** Thanksgiving dinner
**Details:**

## Main Idea/Details

Directions: Put an X through the picture that does not belong.

**Main idea:** A baseball game

**Details:**

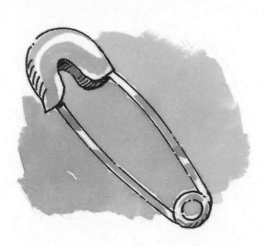

Name _____

## Vocabulary

1. Pat and Matt can hop.

2. Sam has hats and mitts.

3. Nan and Dan can tap.

4. Dad has pots and pans.

*Connecting Words* • **Reading and Writing Workbook**

Name _____

Vocabulary

1. Dan was mad and sad.

2. Sam and Tim are in the sand.

3. Mom or Dad has stamps.

4. Matt and Tam are in a pit.

Directions: Have the children read each sentence and circle the connecting words. Then have them write their own sentence using a connecting word.

_____

- - - - - - - - - - - - - - - - - - - -

_____

- - - - - - - - - - - - - - - - - - - -

_____

## Grammar

Directions: Have the children read each sentence and circle the verb.

1. Sam hit the hat.

2. Nan sat on a mat.

3. The top spins.

4. Dan hops into the pit.

Verbs • **Reading and Writing Workbook**

## Grammar

Directions: Have the children read the words in the box; then, read each sentence and write the verb that fits the sentence.

| pat | hops | sits | spins |
|-----|------|------|-------|

_____

1. Pam and Sam _____ Nan.

_____

2. Dad _____ the top.

_____

3. Tim _____ up on the mat.

_____

4. Spot _____ on the hat.

## Sounds and Spellings

b

b

b

B

## Writing Words and Sentences

bib        bands

A bat was a bit sad.

Directions: Practice writing B and b. Then copy the words and the sentence.

## Reading and Writing

Directions: Write the word that matches each picture. Then write the sentence shown by the picture.

bat

bats

bit

_____

_____

pin

pit

_____

pan

_____

Sid sat in the sand.

Nan and Sid had a pin.

_____

_____

_____

_____

## Sounds and Spellings

Directions: Practice writing c and C. Then copy the words and the sentence.

c

c

C

## Writing Words and Sentences

cat _____  cap _____

Can the cat tap on the can?

## Writing Words

Directions: Write the word for each picture under the picture. Then choose words from under the pictures to complete the sentences.

_____

- - - - - - - - - - - - - - -

_____

_____

- - - - - - - - - - - - - - -

_____

_____

- - - - - - - - - - - - - - -

_____

_____

- - - - - - - - - - - - - - -

_____

_____

- - - - - - - - - - - - - - -

_____

_____

- - - - - - - - - - - - - - -

_____

Nan can pat the _____.

_____

- - - - - - - - - - - -

Pam has a _____.

**Reading and Writing Workbook • *Blending***

**55**

Directions: Have the children read the words in the box; then, read each sentence and write the word that fits the sentence. In some cases, either word will fit.

| in | on |
|----|----|

1. Dan is _____ the pit.

2. Nan is _____ bed.

3. The cat is _____ the mat.

4. Spot is _____ the hat.

**Vocabulary**

Directions: Have the children read and draw a picture for each sentence

1. The can is in the bin.

2. The hat is on the can.

Directions: Write the word from the box that goes with each picture.

| hand | cat | pan | mop | band | pin |
|------|-----|-----|-----|------|-----|

_____

_____

_____

_____

_____

Dan has a _____.

cap
cat

_____

Pat has a _____.

mop
mitt

_____

Bob has a _____.

hand
band

## Sounds and Spellings

c
ck

s      st      p      t

_ack     _ick     _ock

# Reading and Writing Sentences

Directions: Write the sentence that describes the picture.

Dick has socks in the sack.
Pat picks a stick in the stack.

Mack packs a snack.
Stan stacks the sticks.

## Sounds and Spellings

r

r

r

R

## Writing Words and Sentences

rip _____    trip _____

A rat hit the cat and ran.

Name _____

Brad ran on the ramp.
The rabbit is in the crib.

_____

_____

_____

_____

Min ran at camp.
Tim is on a trip.

_____

_____

Sid stands in the sand.
Sid can stand on his hands.

_____

_____

_____

_____

**Reading and Writing Workbook • Blending**

Name _____

## Sounds and Spellings

u

u _____

U _____

## Writing Words and Sentences

bud _____  drum _____

The duck is stuck in the mud.

_____

_____

*Vowel Sounds and Spelling* • **Reading and Writing Workbook**

Directions: Practice writing *u* and *U*. Then copy the words and the sentence.

## Reading and Writing Sentences

Directions: Copy the sentence that describes each picture.

Pam scrubs the pup's hut.
Pam has a pup.

_____

- - - - - - - - - - - - - - - - - -

_____

Bud is in the sun.
The mutt runs up the pump.

_____

- - - - - - - - - - - - - - - - - -

_____

Nan can scrub the tub.
Nan drops her duck in the tub.

_____

- - - - - - - - - - - - - - - - - -

_____

- - - - - - - - - - - - - - - - - -

1. Tam and Dan are (not sad, sad).

2. It is (not hot, hot).

3. It is (fun, not fun).

## Drawing Conclusions

Directions: Read each sentence to the children. Have the children circle Yes or No to tell whether the sentence is true or not true

1. The children are at home.      Yes      No

2. They are painting.      Yes      No

3. They are sad.      Yes      No

# Adjectives

Directions: Write the word that goes with each picture.

| sick | big | mad | sad |

_____

_____

_____

_____

*Adjectives* • **Reading and Writing Workbook**

## Adjectives

Matt is a sad pup.

Min is sick.

Tom is a big cat.

Mom is not mad.

Name _____

## Sounds and Spellings

g

g
G

## Writing Words and Sentences

gas _____    grab _____

The pig is big.

## Writing Words

Directions: Write the words represented in the picture.

pig

sag

grin

_____    _____

- - - - - - - - - - - -    - - - - - - - - - - - -

_____    _____

tag

dig

big

_____    _____

- - - - - - - - - - - -    - - - - - - - - - - - -

_____    _____

**End Punctuation**

1. Pam has a cat ____

2. The cat is little ____

3. They are on a mat ____

4. Pam likes the cat ____

*End Punctuation* • **Reading and Writing Workbook**

## End Punctuation

Directions: Read each sentence. Put a period at the end of each one.

1. Tam has a dog ____

2. The dog is big ____

3. Tam likes his dog ____

4. The dog likes Tam ____

Name _____

Review

Directions: Look at each picture and finish each sentence with the appropriate word.

_____

Rod sat on a _____.

dock
rock

_____

Bob has a _____.

bug
rug

_____

Rob has a _____.

stick
pick

*Sounds and Spellings* • Reading and Writing Workbook

# Review

Directions: Write the word from each box that goes with each picture.

| dog | bag | duck | bug | hen | pig |

_____

- - - - - - - - - - - - - - - -

_____

_____

- - - - - - - - - - - - - - - -

_____

Name _____

## Sounds and Spellings

j
■dge

_____

j _____

J _____

## Writing Words and Sentences

job _____ judge _____

just _____ badge _____

Jack cut the fudge.

_____

*Consonant Sounds and Spellings* • **Reading and Writing Workbook**

Name _____

## Decoding and Spelling

Jack jogs across the bridge.
Jan jumps across the ditch.

_____
- - - - - - - - - - - - - - - - - -
_____

- - - - - - - - - - - - - - - - - -
_____

## Dictation and Spelling

_____    _____
- - - - - - - - - - - - -    - - - - - - - - - - - - -
_____    _____

- - - - - - - - - - - - -    - - - - - - - - - - - - -
_____    _____

- - - - - - - - - - - - - - - - - - - - - - - - - - - -
_____

- - - - - - - - - - - - - - - - - - - - - - - - - - - -
_____

**Reading and Writing Workbook** • *Decoding/Spelling*

## Sounds and Spellings

f

f

F

## Writing Words and Sentences

fan _____

fat _____

Can the fat cat fit in the hat?

Directions: Practice writing *f* and *F*; then copy the words and the sentence.

*Consonant Sounds and Spellings* • **Reading and Writing Workbook**

# Reading and Writing

Directions: Write the letter or sound represented by each *Sound/Spelling Card* picture to form a word.

**Reading and Writing Workbook** • *Blending*

## Sounds and Spellings

Directions: Practice writing e and E; then copy the words and the sentence.

e

e

E

## Writing Words and Sentences

hen

tent

neck

shed

The egg is in a bed.

*Vowel Sounds and Spellings* • **Reading and Writing Workbook**

## Writing Words

Directions: First, label each picture. Then, complete the sentence. Finally, write the spelling represented by the **Sound/Spelling Card** pictures to form a word.

  _____

  _____

  _____

  _____

  _____

  _____

  _____

  _____

_____

The man has _____ hats.

Name _____

## Classify

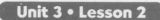

*Classify/Categorize* • **Reading and Writing Workbook**

Name _____

# Classify

Directions: Draw a line from each animal on the left to the one that goes with it on the right.

Name _____

## Sounds and Spellings

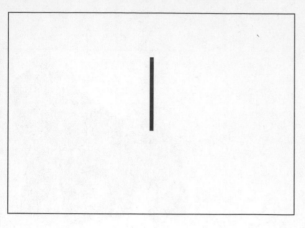

l

l

L

## Writing Words and Sentences

last _____ tickle _____

Bill slips in the puddle.

_____

_____

_____

_____

*Consonant Sounds and Spellings* • **Reading and Writing Workbook**

Directions: Practice writing *l* and *L*; then copy the words and the sentence.

Name _____

## Reading and Writing Sentences

Lil fills the pickle jar.
Lil has lots of dolls.

_____

- - - - - - - - - - - - - - - - - - -

_____

## Dictation and Spelling

_____     _____

- - - - - - - - - - - - - - -     - - - - - - - - - - - - - - -

_____     _____

- - - - - - - - - - - - - - -     - - - - - - - - - - - - - - -

_____     _____

_____

- - - - - - - - - - - - - - - - - - -

_____

- - - - - - - - - - - - - - - - - - -

_____

Name _____

**Inflectional Endings: -ed**

_____

1. The hen _____ the sand.

             peck

_____

2. Dad _____ the dog.

        call

_____

3. The cat _____ the pan.

        lick

_____

4. Sam _____ the bus.

        miss

*Inflectional Endings: -ed* • **Reading and Writing Workbook**

## Inflectional Endings: -ed

Directions: Rewrite each underlined word adding -ed to show something that happened in the past.

1. I stack the rugs. _____

2. Mom and I snack. _____

3. The dogs jump over the fence. _____

4. I hand Jan the fan. _____

Directions: Write the word that goes with each picture.

| bridge | bell | sled | leg | ball | fell |

_____

_____

_____

_____

_____

_____

*Review* • **Reading and Writing Workbook**

# Listening for Consonants

Directions: Write the name of each picture beneath the consonant that is contained in that word.

| l | f |
|---|---|
| | |
| | |
| | |

# Writing Words

| gift | stamp | ramp | tent | fist | sled |
|------|-------|------|------|------|------|

_____

- - - - - - - - - - - -

_____

_____

- - - - - - - - - - - -

_____

*Spelling: Initial and Final Blends* • **Reading and Writing Workbook**

# Blends

| list | sift | must | soft |

loft _____

lift _____

mist _____

rust _____

# Name _____

## Sounds and Spellings

x

x _____

X _____

## Writing Words and Sentences

fox _____   mix _____

The ax is in the box.

_____

_____

*Consonant Sounds and Spellings* • **Reading and Writing Workbook**

# Listening for Vowels

 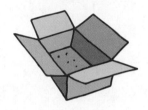 

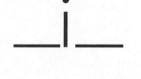 

__i__        __a__        __o__

_____    _____    _____

_____    _____    _____

_____    _____    _____

_____    _____    _____

_____    _____    _____

_____    _____    _____

**Sentence Endings**

Directions: Read the sentences to the children. Have them put a period, question mark, or exclamation point at the end of each sentence.

1. How are you _____

2. You look great _____

3. I am going to the store _____

4. Can we talk _____

5. The shirt is blue _____

6. Wow, what a busy day _____

*Grammar: Sentence Types* • **Reading and Writing Workbook**

## Sentence Endings

Directions: Read the sentences to the children. Have them circle each sentence that is a question and underline each sentence that is an exclamation.

1. I love your hair!

2. Can you paint?

3. What size do you wear?

4. What a cute dog!

5. The tree is tall.

6. Do you like ice cream?

## Sounds and Spellings

Directions: Practice writing z and Z; then copy the words and the sentence.

z

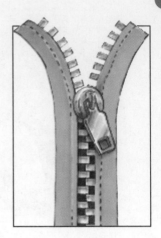

z

Z

## Writing Words and Sentences

zip      buzz

The bug ran in a zigzag.

Name ______________________________

## Word Study

Unit 3 • Lesson 6

Directions: Match the appropriate word for each picture, adding 's to show possession.

Pam    pup    robin    rat

______________ 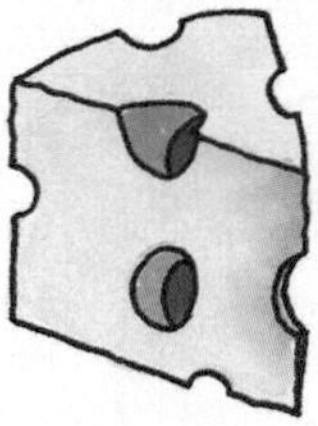 ______________ 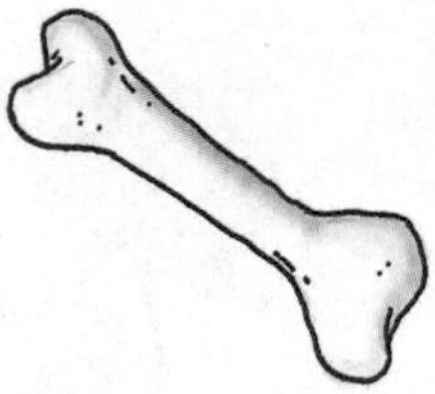

______________ 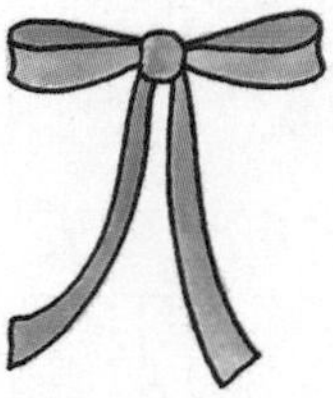 ______________ 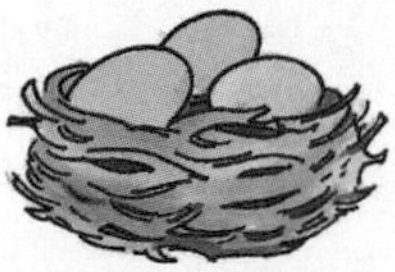

pot    man    cat    lady

______________ 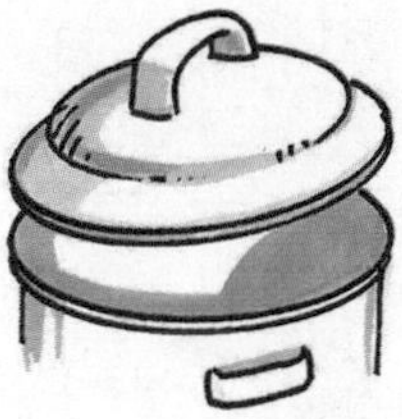 ______________ 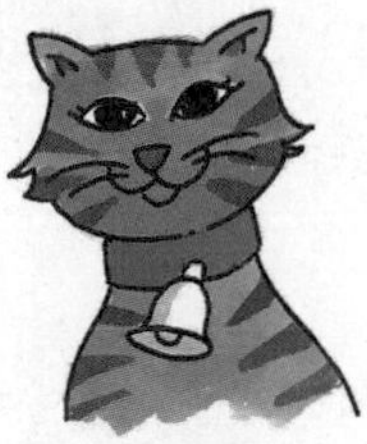

______________ 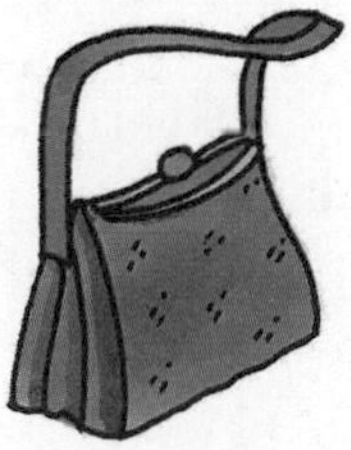 ______________ 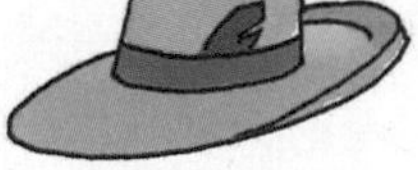

## Sounds and Spellings

box     fan     fox     doll     ball     zip

_____

- - - - - - - - - - - - - - -

_____

_____

- - - - - - - - - - - - - - -

_____

_____

- - - - - - - - - - - - - - -

_____

_____

- - - - - - - - - - - - - - -

_____

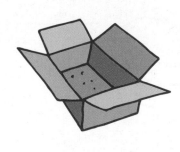

_____

- - - - - - - - - - - - - - -

_____

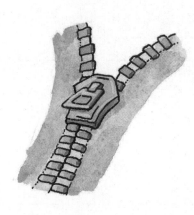

_____

- - - - - - - - - - - - - - -

_____

*Review* • Reading and Writing Workbook

## Sounds and Spellings

Directions: Look at the pictures and finish the sentences with the appropriate word.

_____

Tam has a _____.

duck
doll

_____

Sam has a _____.

ball
bell

## Dictation and Spelling

_____    _____

_____    _____

_____    _____

_____    _____

Name _____

**Capital Letters**

Directions: Read the sentences to the children. Have them draw a line under each word that should begin with a capital letter.

1. sam and liz rode bikes on saturday.

2. it was a sunny june day.

3. they went past green park.

4. then they rode up vine street.

5. at last they got to hill school.

*Reading and Writing Skills Practice* • **Reading and Writing Workbook**

Name _____

## Capital Letters

6. Ben's birthday is in <u>june</u>.

_____

_____

7. <u>ben</u> got a dog.

_____

_____

8. His dog is <u>spot</u>.

_____

_____

9. Spot likes <u>mill park</u>.

_____

_____

10. He likes to run in the <u>grass</u>.

_____

_____

11. They went to the park <u>monday</u>.

_____

_____

12. Spot barked at a <u>duck</u>.

_____

_____

13. <u>the</u> duck ran to the pond.

_____

Name _____

## Sounds and Spellings

| sh |  |
|---|---|

## Writing Words and Sentences

shop _____

rash _____

mash _____

lash _____

Shannon has six shells in a box.

_____

_____

_____

_____

# Writing Words

Directions: Match each word to the appropriate picture; then write the spelling represented by each **Sound/Spelling Card** picture to form a word at the bottom.

| dish | ship | shop | fresh | shell | brush | fish |
|------|------|------|-------|-------|-------|------|

_____

_____

_____

_____

_____

Name _____

## Sounds and Spellings

## Writing Words and Sentences

thin _____    that _____

math _____    bath _____

thump _____

This is a thick cloth.

_____

_____

_____

_____

Name _____

Directions: Unscramble the words to form a sentence that describes the picture.

| slips | the | Bill | on | mud. |

_____

- - - - - - - - - - - - - - - - - - - - - - - - -

_____

## Dictation and Spelling

_____     _____

- - - - - - - - - - - -     - - - - - - - - - - - -

_____     _____

_____     _____

- - - - - - - - - - - -     - - - - - - - - - - - -

_____     _____

_____     _____

- - - - - - - - - - - -     - - - - - - - - - - - -

_____     _____

Name _____

## Sounds and Spellings

th
sh

## Writing Words and Sentences

thick _____     than _____

trash _____     shop _____

both _____     shut _____

She left the trash in the shop.

_____

_____

_____

*Review Sounds and Spellings* • **Reading and Writing Workbook**

## Listening for Consonant Blends

| sh | th |
|---|---|
| | |
| | |
| | |
| | |

## ch
## ■tch

## Writing Words and Sentences

fetch _____     itch _____

ditch _____

catch _____

Mitch catches the pitch.

_____

_____

_____

_____

# Name _____

## Writing Words

| fetch | patches | crutches | catch | ditch | scratch |

_____   _____   _____
- - - - - - - - - - - - -   - - - - - - - - - - - - -   - - - - - - - - - - - - -
_____   _____   _____

## Dictation and Spelling

_____   _____
- - - - - - - - - - - - -   - - - - - - - - - - - - -
_____   _____
_____   _____
- - - - - - - - - - - - -   - - - - - - - - - - - - -
_____   _____
_____
- - - - - - - - - - - - -
_____

Directions: Say the name of each picture. Draw a line to the word that spells its name.

1.  •

• check

2.  •

• thimble

3.  •

• shelf

4.  •

• watch

5.  •

• path

6.  •

• bench

7.  •

• ship

8. •

• crutch

**Spelling**

Directions: Say the name of the picture. Choose the digraph that will complete the picture name. Write the digraph on the line.

9.

ell

ch    sh    th

10.

wa

tch    th    sh

11.

ale

th    sh    wh

12.

lun

ch    sh    th

Name _____

## Sounds and Spellings

# ar

## Writing Words and Sentences

 _____

 _____

 _____

_____

The car is in the barn.

_____

- - - - - - - - - - - - - - - - - - - - - - - -

_____

- - - - - - - - - - - - - - - - - - - - - - - -

_____

*Consonant Sounds and Spellings* • **Reading and Writing Workbook**

## Writing Words

Directions: Look at the picture. Write the words in the list that appear in the picture. Then name other objects in the picture. Circle the words with the ar sound.

alarm

star

ram

barn

man

rabbit

frog

ax

_____    _____    _____

_____    _____    _____

_____    _____    _____

_____    _____    _____

_____    _____    _____

_____    _____    _____

**Reading and Writing Workbook • *Blending***

| mug | fox | tent | sack | pin | nut |
| --- | --- | --- | --- | --- | --- |

_____

- - - - - - - - - - -

_____

_____

- - - - - - - - - - -

_____

_____

- - - - - - - - - - -

_____

_____

- - - - - - - - - - -

_____

_____

- - - - - - - - - - -

_____

_____

- - - - - - - - - - -

_____

## Review

_____

Dan has a pet _____.

frog
fish

_____

Nan's dog can _____.

fetch
match

## Dictation and Spelling

_____     _____

_____     _____

_____     _____

Name _____

## Sounds and Spellings

Directions: Practice writing w and W; then copy the words and the sentence in the spaces provided.

w

w

W

## Writing Words and Sentences

wet       wag

win       well

Will won a wagon.

*Consonant Sounds and Spellings* • **Reading and Writing Workbook**

Name _____

*Directions: Copy the words and the sentence in the spaces provided.*

## Writing Words and Sentences

when

what

whip

When will Jim whip the eggs?

Name _____

**Spelling**

| who | wish | wash | when |

1. Dan must _____ the dishes.

2. _____ is the best catcher?

3. _____ is lunch?

4. I _____ that I had a ship.

*Spelling: wh/ and /w/ Controlled Vowels* • **Reading and Writing Workbook**

Directions: Write the word that best completes each sentence.

| who | what | where | why |

1. _____ is Dick sad?

2. _____ got Nan's socks?

3. _____ did Liz get?

4. _____ did Tam put the box?

Name _____

## Sounds and Spellings

er
i̇r
ur

## Writing Words and Sentences

her _____    bird _____

girl _____    fern _____

curl _____    turn _____

Bert had a burger for supper.

_____

_____

_____

## Unscrambling Sentences

| has | girl | a |
|-----|------|---|
| The | turtle. | little |

_____

- - - - - - - - - - - - - - - - - - - - - - - - - - - -

_____

- - - - - - - - - - - - - - - - - - - - - - - - - - - -

_____

## Dictation and Spelling

_____      _____

- - - - - - - - - - - - - -      - - - - - - - - - - - - - -

_____      _____

- - - - - - - - - - - - - -      - - - - - - - - - - - - - -

_____      _____

- - - - - - - - - - - - - -      - - - - - - - - - - - - - -

_____      _____

# Spelling

| sander | runner | washer | catcher |

_____

_____

_____

_____

*Spelling: /-er/ Endings* • **Reading and Writing Workbook**

Name

Spelling



Directions: Rewrite each word adding *-er* to tell what each person is.

bank

print

farm

pitch

wash

catch

| turtle | bird | catch | girl | wag | whisk |

_____

- - - - - - - - - - -

_____

_____

- - - - - - - - - - -

_____

Name _____

_____

Bob has a pet _____.

| turtle |
| bird |

_____

Pat has a red _____.

| wagon |
| dragon |

## Dictation and Spelling

_____    _____

_____    _____

_____    _____

_____

_____

_____

Directions: Look at the pictures and finish the sentences with the correct words

bird    brim

grill    girl

self    sled

sacks    slacks

stick    slick

press    purse

dunk    duck

belt    bell

corn    cost

*Internal Consonants* • **Reading and Writing Workbook**

Directions: Read the sentences. Write *r* or *l* on the lines to complete the words.

I. Bob has a pu ____ ple wagon.

2. Pat and Bill cu ____ l ribbon.

3. Dad bui ____ ds a big box.

4. Bill has fi ____ m for his camera.

5. Carol plants a bush in her ga ____ den.

6. Pat fixes a sa ____ ad for the picnic.

Name _____

## Sounds and Spellings

k

k _____

K _____

## Writing Words and Sentences

kick _____    bark _____

silk _____    kettle _____

The kitten laps milk.

_____

_____

*Consonant Sounds and Spellings* • **Reading and Writing Workbook**

## Writing Words

Directions: Match a word to each picture.

| park | milk | skirt | mask | skillet | kettle |

_____

_____

_____

_____

_____

_____

**Main Idea**: Day at the Beach
**Details**:

## Main Idea and Details

Directions: Put an X through the picture that does not belong.

**Main Idea:** Nighttime
**Details:**

Name _____

Spelling

Directions: Read the sentences. For each sentence, find the correct word above and write it on the line.

| sick | deck | chicken | truck | water | check |
| --- | --- | --- | --- | --- | --- |

1. May I have a glass of _____?

2. Tess feels _____ today.

3. We must _____ the clock.

4. We have a _____ to sit on.

5. The men put gas in the _____.

6. Tom will fix _____ for dinner.

**132**

*Consonant Sounds and Spellings* • **Reading and Writing Workbook**

Directions: Read each sentence. Circle the word that is spelled correctly. Write the word on the line.

_____

1. We must _____ the door.

lock    lok

_____

2. Sam can _____ a basket of nuts.

pik    pick

_____

3. He hurt his _____.

neck    leak

_____

4. We will camp on the _____.

dec    deck

_____

5. The _____ pecked in the sand.

chick    check

## Sounds and Spellings

Directions: Copy the words and the sentences in the spaces provided.

### Writing Words and Sentences

sing _____  thing _____

ring _____  wing _____

He rang a gong.

_____

_____

We sang a song.

_____

_____

The string is tangled.
The string is in a box.

_____

- - - - - - - - - - - - - - - -

_____

He plays ping pong.
He plays on the swing.

_____

- - - - - - - - - - - - - - - -

## Dictation and Spelling

_____   _____

- - - - - - - - - - - -   - - - - - - - - - - - -

_____   _____

- - - - - - - - - - - -   - - - - - - - - - - - -

_____   _____

- - - - - - - - - - - -

_____

- - - - - - - - - - - - - - - - - - - - - - - - - - - -

_____

Name _____

Spelling

Directions: Look at the pictures. On the line, write ng or nk to complete each word.

ki____

sku____

tru____

stro____

wi____

ri____

ba____

swi____

si____

*Consonant Sounds and Spellings* • **Reading and Writing Workbook**

**Spelling**

Directions: Read the sentences. Circle the correct word. Write the word on the line.

1. Thad can _____ well.

   sink    sing

2. Nora _____ her hat on the hanger.

   hunk    hung

3. Do you _____ it will snow today?

   think    thing

4. The doctor put Ted's hurt arm in a _____.

   slink    sling

5. Did the bee _____ you?

   stink    sting

Name _____

## Sounds and Spellings

qu_

qu _____

Qu _____

## Writing Words and Sentences

quilt _____    quit _____

quick _____    quiz _____

The quilt has stars.

_____

_____

Name ______________________________

## Listening for Words



Directions: Read the words in the boxes; then choose the correct word based on the clues given.

| | | |
|---|---|---|
| ○ quit<br>○ quick<br>○ quilt | ○ market<br>○ check<br>○ quack | ○ liquid<br>○ licked<br>○ locked |
| ○ squint<br>○ squirm<br>○ squiggle | ○ quill<br>○ king<br>○ kick | ○ squirt<br>○ square<br>○ squish |

Directions: Read the story to the children. Have them draw a circle around each quotation mark. Have them draw a line under the exact words the person said.

1. "Look at all the kittens," said Lynn.

2. "I like the little orange one," said Becky.

3. "The gray kitty is sleeping," said Lynn.

4. "Watch the white one drag the blanket," said Becky.

5. "That big one likes to chase the ball," said Lynn.

6. "Oh, all of them are so cute," said Becky.

**Grammar**

1. Let's go to the park,  said Molly.

2. We can take our soccer ball,  said Anna.

3. Pete and I want to go too,  said Tim.

4. We can have two teams,  said Pete.

5. Tim and I will be on one team,  said Molly.

6. Pete and I will be on the other team,  said Anna.

7. Let's race to the park,  said Pete.

8. Okay,  said Molly, Anna, and Tim together.

**Reading and Writing Workbook** • *Quotation Marks*

Name _____

## Sounds and Spellings

y—

y

Y

## Writing Words and Sentences

yarn _____   yes _____

yell _____   yet _____

I eat yellow yams.

*Consonant Sounds and Spellings* • **Reading and Writing Workbook**

Directions: Practice writing and y and Y; then copy the words and the sentence in the spaces provided.

## Reading and Writing Sentences

The dog yelps at the rabbit.
A rabbit nibbles plants in the yard.
The dog naps in the backyard.

## Dictation and Spelling

# Name _____

## Vocabulary

| | | |
|---|---|---|
| nest | track | fill |
| back | will | pest |
| sack | west | mill |

| tack | best | hill |
|---|---|---|

*Word Families* • **Reading and Writing Workbook**

## Vocabulary

Directions: Read the words in each row. Circle the words that belong to the same word family.

1. camp     limp     damp     ramp

2. dust     must     nest     just

3. sniff     whiff     stuff     cliff

4. band     send     mend     lend

5. horn     corn     worn     barn

6. gift     left     drift     sift

Name _____

# Sounds and Spellings

| ring | yarn | kitten | yak | skunk | quilt |

_____

- - - - - - - - - - -

_____

_____

- - - - - - - - - - -

_____

_____

- - - - - - - - - - -

_____

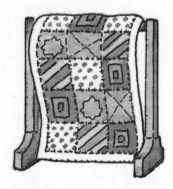

_____

- - - - - - - - - - -

_____

_____

- - - - - - - - - - -

_____

_____

- - - - - - - - - - -

_____

*Review* • **Reading and Writing Workbook**

## Sounds and Spellings

Directions: Look at the pictures and finish the sentences with the appropriate word.

_____

Nan has a _____ on her finger.

| rat |
| ring |

_____

We can smell a _____.

| trunk |
| skunk |

_____

The kitten has the _____.

| yarn |
| barn |

Directions: Add -ed and -ing to each of the words. Write the new words on the lines.

**-ed**                    **-ing**

pin

tap

pet

call

wash

148

*Inflectional Endings -ed, -ing* • **Reading and Writing Workbook**

Name _____

Directions: Add -ed or -ing to the word under each sentence. Write the new word on the line to complete the sentence.

_____

1. Spot _____ off the dock.

slip

_____

2. He _____ in the mud.

stomp

_____

3. Spot's fur is wet and _____.

mat

_____

4. A skunk _____ him.

squirt

_____

5. Spot is _____ on Sam. Oh, Spot!

jump

_____

6. Spot is _____ from Sam.

run

Name _____

## Sounds and Spellings

a
a_e

### Writing Words and Sentences

ape _____

cane _____

late _____

Dave made a mask with paper and tape.

_____

_____

_____

*Long Vowel Sounds and Spellings* • **Reading and Writing Workbook**

Name _____

Directions: Finish each sentence with the appropriate word.

_____
- - - - - - - - -

1. Ted has a _____.

cap
cape

_____
- - - - - - - - -

2. Pat fixed his model _____.

plan
plane

_____
- - - - - - - - -

3. A whale _____ swim.

can
cane

## Dictation and Spelling

_____        _____
- - - - - - - - - - - - -        - - - - - - - - - - - - -

_____        _____

_____        _____
- - - - - - - - - - - - -        - - - - - - - - - - - - -

_____        _____

_____        _____
- - - - - - - - - - - - -        - - - - - - - - - - - - -

_____        _____

Name _____

## Sounds and Spellings

s
ce
ci__

### Writing Words and Sentences

cent _____    cell _____

face _____    city _____

Grace has six cents.

_____

The mice danced.

_____

## Listening for Consonant Sounds

face  cake  race  candle
picnic  carrot  lace  circle

_____

_____

_____

_____

_____

Name _____

## Vocabulary

1.

hand      ball

2.

sun      fish

3. 

back      pack

4. 

bird      bath

5. 

drum      stick

6.

sun      burn

*Compound Words* • **Reading and Writing Workbook**

**Vocabulary**

Directions: Read the sentences. Circle the compound word. On the lines, write the two words that make the compound word.

1. Tess ate a big hunk of watermelon.

_____     _____

- - - - - - - - - - - - -     - - - - - - - - - - - - -

_____     _____

2. Jeb has a sunburn on his neck.

_____     _____

- - - - - - - - - - - - -     - - - - - - - - - - - - -

_____     _____

3. Do not put the bathmat in the tub.

_____     _____

- - - - - - - - - - - - -     - - - - - - - - - - - - -

_____     _____

4. Cam burned her fingertip on a hot pot.

_____     _____

- - - - - - - - - - - - -     - - - - - - - - - - - - -

_____     _____

5. Where are the snapshots of the trip?

_____     _____

- - - - - - - - - - - - -     - - - - - - - - - - - - -

_____     _____

| cake | tape | rake | ape | face | plane |

_____
- - - - - - - - - -
_____

_____
- - - - - - - - - -
_____

_____
- - - - - - - - - -
_____

_____
- - - - - - - - - -
_____

_____
- - - - - - - - - -
_____

_____
- - - - - - - - - -
_____

Name ______________________

## Review



Directions: Use the letters to make word families.

b c m

___ake

sh c dr

___ape

## Dictation and Spelling

Directions: Read the sentences to the children. Have them circle the sentences that are statements. Draw a line under the sentences that are questions. Draw a box around the sentences that are exclamations.

1. Our class went to the zoo.

2. We stood in front of a cage of chimps.

3. One chimp sat on the top branch.

4. Will it swing down to get a banana?

5. A small chimp ate two bananas.

6. May we feed the chimps?

7. Suddenly a big chimp screeched!

8. Everyone jumped!

*Sentence Types* • **Reading and Writing Workbook**

**Grammar**

Directions: Read the story to the children. Have them write the correct end marks.

Bill and I went for a hike___ We walked up a rocky trail___

Look___ There is a little chipmunk___ It is looking at us___

Should we give the chipmunk some peanuts___ Will it come

to us___ No, it is going up the tree___

**Sounds and Spellings**

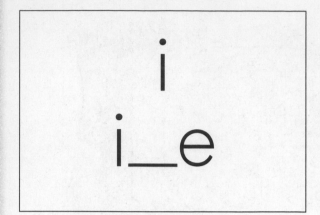

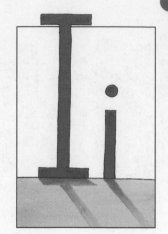

Directions: Copy the words and the sentences in the spaces provided.

## Writing Words and Sentences

tiger _____     title _____

time _____     mile _____

Nine fish swim by.

_____

_____

Did he find a dime?

_____

_____

## Completing Sentences

Directions: Complete each sentence with the appropriate word.

1. I like to _____ my bike.

2. Did you _____ the page?

3. Dad made a _____ dinner.

4. The man was gentle and _____.

5. The lamp is _____.

6. Do not let the dog _____.

rid
ride

rip
ripe

fin
fine

kin
kind

dim
dime

bit
bite

Directions: Read each sentence. Look at the underlined words. Find the word that means the opposite and write it on the line.

| give | there | catch | small | on | well |

1. Mike will <u>toss</u> the ball so Dan can _____ it.

2. Please <u>take</u> this tape and _____ it to Nan.

3. Ann will stand <u>here</u> and Sue will stand _____.

4. Mark is <u>sick</u>, but Jill is _____.

5. Beth's cupcake is <u>big</u>. Mine is _____.

6. You get <u>off</u> the slide. I will get _____.

## Vocabulary

> well   small   bottom   pull
> last   thin   on   start

Directions: Read the words. Find the word that means the opposite and write it on the line.

1. big _____

2. stop _____

3. first _____

4. push _____

5. off _____

6. thick _____

7. top _____

8. sick _____

## Sounds and Spellings

Directions: Copy the words and the sentences in the spaces provided.

o
o_e

## Writing Words and Sentences

no _____ rode _____

hold _____ stone _____

The dog hid a bone.

_____

- - - - - - - - - - - - - -

_____

I broke the phone.

_____

- - - - - - - - - - - - - -

_____

Name _____

## Sounds and Spellings

○ April

○ open

○ oval

○ hop

○ hope

○ hold

○ block

○ bone

○ broke

## Dictation and Spelling

_____ _____

_____ _____

_____ _____

_____ _____

Directions: Write the word that goes with each picture.

| tail | hay | nail | crayon | sail | mail |

_____

- - - - - - - - - - - - - - - - -

_____

_____

- - - - - - - - - - - - - - - - -

_____

_____

- - - - - - - - - - - - - - - - -

_____

_____

- - - - - - - - - - - - - - - - -

_____

_____

- - - - - - - - - - - - - - - - -

_____

_____

- - - - - - - - - - - - - - - - -

_____

Name _____

Review

Directions: Look at the pictures and finish each sentence with the correct word.

_____

- - - - - - - - - -

I got a letter in the _____.

male

mail

_____

- - - - - - - - - -

Tim has a _____ in his hand.

snail

snake

_____

- - - - - - - - - -

We carry lunch on a _____.

train

tray

**Reading and Writing Workbook •** *Sounds and Spellings*

Name _____

## Review

nine    rope    tape

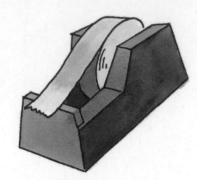

_____    _____    _____

- - - - - - - - -    - - - - - - - - -    - - - - - - - - -

_____    _____    _____

## Dictation and Spelling

_____    _____

- - - - - - - - - - - -    - - - - - - - - - - - -

_____    _____

_____    _____

- - - - - - - - - - - -    - - - - - - - - - - - -

_____    _____

_____    _____

_____    _____

- - - - - - - - - - - - - - - - - - - - - - - - - - - - - - - - - -

_____

**Review**

_____

_ _ _ _ _ _ _ _ _ _ _ _ _

The ducks swam in the _____.

lock
lake

_____

_ _ _ _ _ _ _ _ _ _ _ _ _

Brett ate a dish of _____.

rice
race

_____

_ _ _ _ _ _ _ _ _ _ _ _ _

Joy ate a big _____.

bone
cone

# Grammar

Directions: Read the sentences. Circle the word that tells who or what has something. Then write the word on the line.

1. Jake's dog ate a slipper. _____

2. Martha's roses are pretty. _____

3. Jason's shirt is purple. _____

4. The farmer's truck is red. _____

5. Ken's mother is a nurse. _____

6. Meg's skirt is very long. _____

**Grammar**

Directions: Write the words that tell who has each object. The first one is done for you.

1. Sal has this gift.

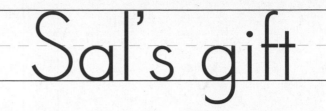

Sal's gift

2. A dog has the bone.

3. Ned rides this bike.

4. The farmer has a hat.

5. Jan made this cake.

6. Tim has this rake.

**Reading and Writing Workbook** • *Possessive Nouns, Apostrophes*

**171**

Name _____

## Sounds and Spellings

v

v

V

## Writing Words and Sentences

vine _____   van _____

brave _____   five _____

Viv has a valentine.

_____

_____

## Completing Sentences

Directions: Finish each sentence with the appropriate word.

| stove | drives | never |
|-------|--------|-------|
| velvet | saves | vase |

_____

1. My mom _____ a van.

_____

2. Jim _____ baseball cards.

_____

3. Jan has a _____ dress.

_____

4. Lance put the pan on the _____.

_____

5. Put the buds in a _____.

Name _____

1. A <u>flock</u> of ducks sat (together) in the park.

2. Sharon's <u>magenta</u> shirt matches her pink shorts.

3. Bob <u>refused</u> the plans when he said no.

4. James <u>towers</u> far above the kids.

5. The <u>plume</u> in his hat is from a bird's wing.

6. The <u>churn</u> will stir and shake milk to make butter.

Name _____

Directions: Read the sentences. Look at the underlined words. Circle the word or words that tell the meaning of the underlined word in each sentence.

1. The <u>brawny</u> man could lift one hundred pounds.

smart                              strong

2. The skirt is too small. You must <u>enlarge</u> it.

make larger          make smaller

3. The dog's <u>speckled</u> fur looks like a dotted cape.

spotted                          striped

4. The <u>stony</u> wall had many flat rocks.

made flat          made of rocks

5. <u>Litter</u> from the garbage can covered the yard.

trash                              sand

6. Her <u>enormous</u> garden covers the backyard.

tiny                              large

## Sounds and Spellings

u

u__e

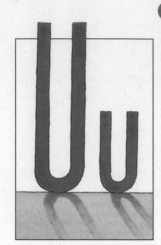

Directions: Copy the words and the sentences in the spaces provided.

## Writing Words and Sentences

huge _____     cute _____

cube _____     use _____

The mule likes music.

_____
_____
_____

Luke has cute cats.

_____
_____
_____

Directions: Write the sentence described by the picture.

The mule has a cute hat.
The mule licks an ice cube.

_____

- - - - - - - - - - - - - - - - - - - - - - - - - -

_____

- - - - - - - - - - - - - - - - - - - - - - - - - -

_____

## Dictation and Spelling

_____

- - - - - - - - - - - - - - - - - - - - - - - - - -

_____

- - - - - - - - - - - - - - - - - - - - - - - - - -

_____

_____

- - - - - - - - - - - - - - - - - - - - - - - - - -

_____

## Sounds and Spellings

Directions: Copy the words and sentence in the spaces provided.

j    ge
    gi_

### Writing Words and Sentences

gem _____    rage _____

just _____    page _____

The gerbil ran into the cage.

_____

_____

_____

## Listening for Consonant Sounds

bag   gentle   bridge   gave

_____    _____

_____    _____

### Dictation and Spelling

_____    _____

_____    _____

## Sounds and Spellings

Directions: Copy the words and sentences in the spaces provided.

e

e__e

Ee

## Writing Words and Sentences

we  _____    even  _____

he  _____    she  _____

Repeat after me.

_____

_____

I had a fever today.

_____

_____

## Sounds and Spellings

Directions: Write the sentence that tells about the picture.

She runs ten meters.
She runs a fever.

_____

- - - - - - - - - - - - - - - - -

Steve has a fever.
Steve ate these eggs.

_____

- - - - - - - - - - - - - - - - -

She is on a trapeze.
She mixes concrele.

_____

- - - - - - - - - - - - - - - - -

bear   bare

whole   hole

son   sun

for   four

to   two

their   there

*Homophones* • **Reading and Writing Workbook**

**Vocabulary**

*Directions: Read each sentence. Circle the correct word. Write the word on the lines.*

_____
- - - - - - - -

1. Can you _____ my socks?

fined   find

_____
- - - - - - - -

2. Where did you dig the _____?

hole   whole

_____
- - - - - - - -

3. Did you find _____ softball?

there   their

_____
- - - - - - - -

4. My dog has _____.

fir   fur

_____
- - - - - - - -

5. If the rain stops, the _____ will shine.

sun   son

Directions: Write the word that goes with each picture.

bridge    ruler    she    cage    vine    mule

_____

- - - - - - - - - - -

_____

_____

- - - - - - - - - - -

_____

_____

- - - - - - - - - - -

_____

_____

- - - - - - - - - - -

_____

_____

- - - - - - - - - - -

_____

_____

- - - - - - - - - - -

_____

*Sounds and Spellings* • **Reading and Writing Workbook**

Directions: Look at the pictures and finish the sentences with the correct word.

Sue sang on the _____.

bridge    stage

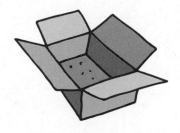

The box was _____.

large    judge

## Dictation and Spelling

cake    jump    athlete    mice    she    mule

_____
- - - - - - - - - - - -
_____

_____
- - - - - - - - - - - -
_____

_____
- - - - - - - - - - - -
_____

_____
- - - - - - - - - - - -
_____

_____
- - - - - - - - - - - -
_____

_____
- - - - - - - - - - - -
_____

Directions: Look at the pictures and finish the sentences with the correct word.

_____

_ _ _ _ _ _ _ _ _ _

_____ got first prize.

He
She

_____

_ _ _ _ _ _ _ _ _ _

The _____ is in the cage.

bird
brim

_____

_ _ _ _ _ _ _ _ _ _

The wall is made of _____.

dirt
concrete

Name _____

## ee
## ea

### Writing Words and Sentences

real _____     meal _____

feel _____     sheep _____

He eats green beans.

_____

_____

The seal fell asleep.

_____

_____

## Writing Opposites

Directions: Write each word next to its opposite on the lines.

| begin | awake | fake | end | real | asleep |

_____

- - - - - - - - - - - - - - - -

_____

- - - - - - - - - - - - - - - -

_____

- - - - - - - - - - - - - - - -

## Dictation and Spelling

_____

- - - - - - - - - - - - - - - -

_____

- - - - - - - - - - - - - - - -

_____

- - - - - - - - - - - - - - - -

**Vocabulary**

| giggle | woman | ill | rush |
| mend | store | plump | scream |

1. Steve is <u>sick</u> today.

2. Mom needs to <u>fix</u> her scarf.

3. That <u>lady</u> made us cookies.

4. The <u>fat</u> pup chases a ball.

5. We must <u>run</u> or we'll be late.

6. Bob's joke made us <u>laugh</u>.

7. They <u>yell</u> for their friends.

8. We can find a gift in that <u>shop</u>.

**Vocabulary**

Directions: Read the words in column 1. For each, find the word in column 2 that means almost the same thing. Draw a line to connect the two words.

1. gentle                    drip

2. jump                      present

3. leak                      kind

4. smile                     begin

5. gift                      leap

6. friend                    grin

7. start                     below

8. hat                       pal

9. fast                      quick

10. under                    cap

**Reading and Writing Workbook • *Synonyms***

Directions: Read the sentences. Circle the verb in each sentence.

1. James tosses the ball to Karen.

2. Amy runs faster than Andy.

3. Charlie jumps up to catch the ball.

4. Sarah yells to her teammate.

5. Devin and Todd race to the bench.

6. Our team scores the most.

7. All of us clap for the winning team.

**Grammar**

Directions: Read each sentence. Then read the two words under each sentence. Choose the verb that will correctly complete the sentence. Write the verb on the line.

_____

1. Vance _____ into the circus tent.

    walks   talks
_____

2. He _____ on the bench.

    stands   sits   _____

3. Crinkle the Clown _____ him a red balloon.

    gives   grabs
_____

4. Vance _____ elephants.

    watches   rides
_____

5. He _____ popcorn and peanuts.

   drinks   eats

    _____

6. The clowns make Vance _____.

    look   laugh
_____

7. Vance _____ when the circus ends.

   claps   hides

## Sounds and Spellings

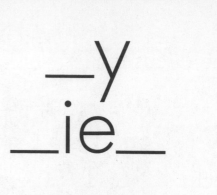

Directions: Copy the words and sentences in the spaces provided.

## Writing Words and Sentences

chief _____    any _____

pony _____    tiny _____

Betty saves pennies.

_____

_____

Sally fed the bunnies.

_____

_____

## Reading and Writing Sentences

Directions: Write the sentence described by each picture.

The lily is white.
The lilies are white.

The box is shiny.
The box is dirty.

The puppy is sleepy.
Puppies are sleepy.

The pony runs away.
The thief runs away.

Name _____

Spelling

1. All of us had _____ to eat at the party.

plenty   plumpy

2. Mort likes _____ over mashed potatoes.

candy   gravy

3. Our dog is too _____ to chase a stick.

tardy   lazy

4. We sat in the _____ part of the park.

grassy   glassy

5. Did her _____ take her to school?

mummy   mommy

**196**        *Sounds and Spellings* • **Reading and Writing Workbook**

# Spelling

| candy | baby | bunny | happy | lily |
|---|---|---|---|---|
| twenty | family | city | puppy | |

_____

_ _ _ _ _ _ _ _ _ _ _ _ _

_____

_____

_ _ _ _ _ _ _ _ _ _ _ _ _

_____

_____

_ _ _ _ _ _ _ _ _ _ _ _ _

_____

_____

_ _ _ _ _ _ _ _ _ _ _ _ _

_____

_____

_ _ _ _ _ _ _ _ _ _ _ _ _

_____

_____

_ _ _ _ _ _ _ _ _ _ _ _ _

_____

_____

_ _ _ _ _ _ _ _ _ _ _ _ _

_____

_____

_ _ _ _ _ _ _ _ _ _ _ _ _

_____

_____

_ _ _ _ _ _ _ _ _ _ _ _ _

_____

**Reading and Writing Workbook** • *Long* e *Spelled* -y

Vocabulary

Directions: Read the words in each row. Draw a circle around the words that rhyme.

1. treat     team     seat     heat

2. cage     page     stage     cape

3. like     bake     make     cake

4. hand     band     stand     pond

5. pack     sock     rack     stack

6. match     stitch     pitch     ditch

7. small     fall     mill     stall

8. just     must     trust     blast

9. seam     bean     mean     clean

10. truck     cluck     brick     stuck

*Rhyming Words* • **Reading and Writing Workbook**

## Vocabulary

| still | stick | blink | lap | log | sap | dog |
| best | trick | thrill | chest | clang | think | rang |

1. trap

2. jog

3. will

4. nest

5. sang

6. brick

7. pink

Directions: Write the word that goes with each picture.

tire    cheer    shore    hear    square    core

_____

- - - - - - - - - - - - - - -

_____

_____

- - - - - - - - - - - - - - -

_____

_____

- - - - - - - - - - - - - - -

_____

_____

- - - - - - - - - - - - - - -

_____

_____

- - - - - - - - - - - - - - -

_____

_____

- - - - - - - - - - - - - - -

_____

**Phonics**

Directions: Look at the pictures and finish the sentences with the correct word.

_____

Amy _____ a dress.

tore    wore

_____

Pups _____ at a bug.

stare    sneer

## Dictation and Spelling

_____    _____

_____    _____

_____    _____

_____    _____

Directions: Remove the -y and add -ies to make each word mean more than one. Write the word on the line.

1. baby _____

2. puppy _____

3. family _____

4. bunny _____

5. lady _____

6. candy _____

Name _____

1. The little cub ate all of the _____ .

   berrys    berries

2. The puppy's muddy feet _____ the rug.

   dirtyed    dirtied

3. Gretchen _____ about the lost tape.

   worried    worryed

4. The _____ are asleep in the basket.

   puppys    puppies

5. Jane _____ to her friend's letter.

   replied    replyed

6. The hotel has three _____ .

   lobbys    lobbies

## Sounds and Spellings

Directions: Copy the words and the sentences in the spaces provided.

ai__
__ay

Aa

## Writing Words and Sentences

pail _____    snail _____

pay _____    stay _____

The raisins are stale.

_____

_____

It is Kay's birthday.

_____

_____

*Vowel Sounds and Spellings* • **Reading and Writing Workbook**

# Homophones

pale    pail

_____

_ _ _ _ _ _ _ _ _

_____

sail    sale

_____

_ _ _ _ _ _ _ _ _

_____

tale    tail

_____

_ _ _ _ _ _ _ _ _

_____

male    mail

_____

_ _ _ _ _ _ _ _ _

_____

waist    waste

_____

_ _ _ _ _ _ _ _ _

_____

plane    plain

_____

_ _ _ _ _ _ _ _ _

_____

## Compare and Contrast

Directions: Circle the thing in each row that is different.

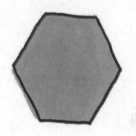 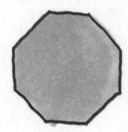 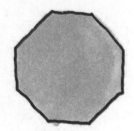 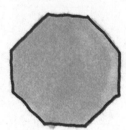

cdgt     cdgt     cgdt     cdgt

## Compare and Contrast

Directions: Circle the word or words that tell how the animals are alike.

four legs          pet

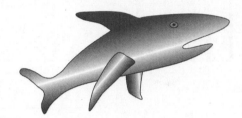

swim          no legs

live in nest          have fur

**Sounds and Spellings**

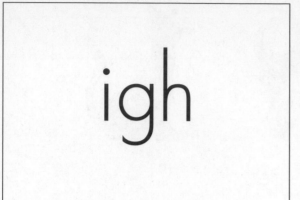

Directions: Copy the words and the sentences in the spaces proveided.

**Writing Words and Sentences**

high _____   sigh _____

sight _____   flight _____

The light is bright.

_____

- - - - - - - - - - - - - - - - - - - - -

_____

You might be right.

_____

- - - - - - - - - - - - - - - - - - - - -

_____

## Writing Compound Words

| | |
|---|---|
| light | shirt |
| night | cut |
| hair | rope |
| tight | bulb |

## Dictation and Spelling

over   on   between   under   in   behind

1. The squirrel sits _____ the log.

2. A cat walks _____ the dishes.

3. The dog stands _____ the fence.

4. The gerbil hides _____ the paper.

5. The jellyfish swims _____ the shells.

6. A bird finds a worm _____ a tree.

*Position Words* • **Reading and Writing Workbook**

Directions: Look at each picture. Read each sentence. Write the correct word to describe where the object is located.

Name _____

Directions: Read each sentence. Circle the words that tell where things are located.

1. Dad puts the picnic basket in the car.

2. We drive over the hill to the park.

3. Randy puts the basket on the table.

4. Susie sits under a tree and reads.

5. Dad sets his chair in front of the grill.

6. We put the game between us on the grass.

7. Mom takes the snacks out of the basket.

8. Randy hides behind a bush.

dime   stone   tree   smile   puppy   bone

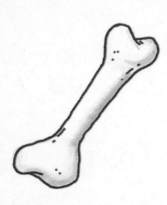

_____

- - - - - - - - - - - -

_____

_____

- - - - - - - - - - - -

_____

Review

_____

_ _ _ _ _ _ _ _ _ _ _ _ _ _ _

She smelled the _____.

bows
rose

_____

_ _ _ _ _ _ _ _ _ _ _ _ _ _ _

Jane went to the _____.

park
beach

_____

_ _ _ _ _ _ _ _ _ _ _ _ _ _ _

Dan broke his _____.

nose
toes

**Reading and Writing Workbook** • *Sounds and Spellings*

Directions: Copy the words and sentences in the spaces provided.

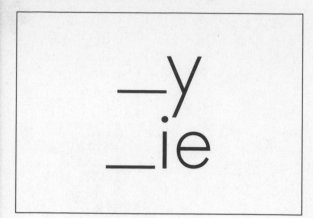

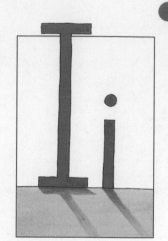

## Writing Words and Sentences

try _____    tries _____

fly _____    flies _____

Birds fly in the sky.

_____

_ _ _ _ _ _ _ _ _ _ _ _ _

_____

He tries the pie.

_____

_ _ _ _ _ _ _ _ _ _ _ _ _

_____

## Sounds and Spellings

Directions: Write the correct word in each blank.

| fly | tie | tries | pie | sky |

_____

1. The _____ buzzes past my head.

_____

2. I ate the cherry _____ all by myself.

_____

3. Tyrone _____ to do a trick.

## Dictation and Spelling

_____  _____

_____  _____

_____  _____

_____  _____

_____  _____

_____  _____

Directions: Read each sentence. Look at the underlined word. Circle the word that means the same thing as the underlined word.

1. We must <u>hustle</u> to get to the movie on time.

       rush     wait

2. Debbie ate breakfast <u>prior to</u> going to work.

      before     after

3. The <u>drenched</u> puppy dripped puddles all over the rug.

      dry     wet

4. Everyone must <u>cease</u> talking so we can hear the song.

      begin     stop

5. Can you help me with this <u>difficult</u> question?

      easy     hard

6. Greg was so <u>weary</u> that he fell asleep in the chair.

      awake     tired

## Vocabulary

Directions: Read each sentence. Look at the underlined word. Circle the word or words in the sentence that help you understand what the underlined word means.

1. Jan's <u>merry</u> face showed that she was happy with

her new pet.

2. The ape is so <u>huge</u> that it fills the cage.

### Dictation and Spelling

_____   _____

_____   _____

_____   _____

_____   _____

## Sounds and Spellings

Directions: Copy the words and sentences in the spaces provided.

o
oe

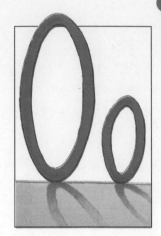

## Writing Words and Sentences

no _____     doe _____

toe _____     Joe _____

Joe will hoe the garden.

_____

_____

_____

*Long Vowel Sounds and Spellings* • **Reading and Writing Workbook**

## Listening for Words

Directions: Read the words in the boxes. Fill in the circle next to each word that has the long o sound. Complete the sentence using the letters represented in the pictures.

○ oboe

○ open

○ oval

○ Joe

○ joke

○ job

○ block

○ bone

○ broke

○ too

○ toe

○ tone

○ not

○ no

○ nose

○ go

○ got

○ gold

_____

A worm has _____ feet.

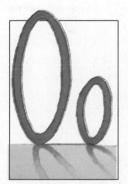

## Sounds and Spellings

o
oa_

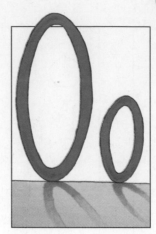

Directions: Copy the words and sentence in the spaces provided.

### Writing Words and Sentences

soap _____ oat _____

A toad ate my toast.

_____

- - - - - - - - - - - - - - -

_____

### Dictation and Spelling

_____

- - - - - - - - - - - - - - -

_____

- - - - - - - - - - - - - - -

_____

**Sounds and Spellings**

_ow
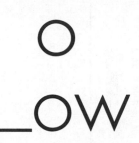

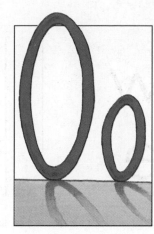

**Writing Words and Sentences**

grow _____     row _____

yellow _____

The snow blows past the window.

_____

_____

_____

_____

**Sounds and Spellings**

u ew
_ue

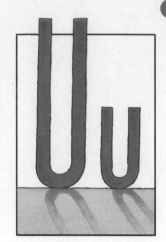

Directions: Copy the words and the sentence on the spaces provided.

**Writing Words and Sentences**

few _____     cue _____

pew _____     hue _____

The firefighter rescued the cat.

_____

_____

_____

## Sounds and Spellings

Directions: Fill in the blank with the correct word.

| use | mule | amuse | rescue | few |
|-----|------|-------|--------|-----|

1. He will _____ the cat from **the tree**.

2. We rode a _____ down the trail.

3. There are only a _____ seconds left.

4. The puppet will _____ you.

5. You can _____ a hammer and nails **to build it**.

**Reading and Writing Workbook** • *Vowel Sounds and Spellings*

Directions: Write the word that goes with each picture.

fly    boat    pie    toe    coat    bow

_____

- - - - - - - - - - -

_____

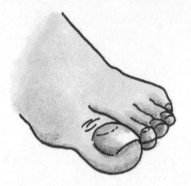

_____

- - - - - - - - - - -

_____

_____

- - - - - - - - - - -

_____

_____

- - - - - - - - - - -

_____

_____

- - - - - - - - - - -

_____

_____

- - - - - - - - - - -

_____

Name _____

## Review

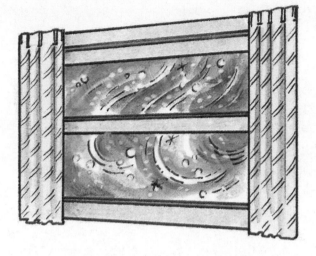

_____

The _____ fell outside.

rain

snow

## Dictation and Spelling

_____

_____

_____

_____

_____

_____

Directions: Look at the picture and finish the sentence with the correct word.

Name _____

## Sounds and Spellings

oo u_e
_ue ew
u

## Writing Words and Sentences

food _____   flute _____

glue _____   tuba _____

judo _____   blue _____

The balloon floats up to the moon.

_____

_____

_____

Writing Words

_____

1. He huffed and he puffed and he blew it down.

_____

_____

2. The farmer's goose honked at me. _____

_____

_____

3. I saw a cocoon on a leaf. _____

_____

4. She made a nest for bluebirds.

_____

_____

5. Do you have the rules of the game?

_____

Dictation and Spelling

_____     _____

_____     _____

_____     _____

_____     _____

_____

## Sounds and Spellings

Directions: Copy the words and sentences on the lines.

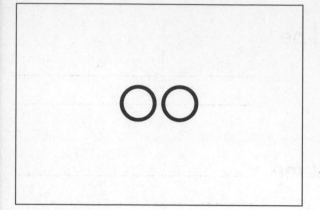

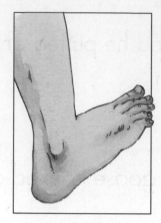

### Writing Words and Sentences

# brook _____

# hood _____

Ed shook his foot.

_____

_____

I took the book.

_____

_____

*Vowel Sounds and Spellings* • **Reading and Writing Workbook**

Name_____

Directions: Write the sentence described by the picture.

Ned wears a hood.
Ned chops wood.

_____

- - - - - - - - - - - - - - -

_____

Susan reads a book.
Susan tries to cook.

_____

- - - - - - - - - - - - - - -

_____

Tom hangs his coat on a hook.
Tom sits by a brook.

_____

- - - - - - - - - - - - - - -

_____

Directions: Write the word that goes with each object.

| truck | bird | plane | bee |
| jet | motorcycle | car | bike |

## wheels

_____

- - - - - - - - - - - -

_____

_____

- - - - - - - - - - - -

_____

_____

- - - - - - - - - - - -

_____

_____

- - - - - - - - - - - -

_____

## wings

_____

- - - - - - - - - - - -

_____

_____

- - - - - - - - - - - -

_____

_____

- - - - - - - - - - - -

_____

_____

- - - - - - - - - - - -

_____

*Classify/Categorize* • **Reading and Writing Workbook**

# Name_____

## Classifying

| sock | brush | cookies | shoe |
|------|-------|---------|------|
| milk | bat | comb | ball |

_____         _____

_____  and  _____


_____         _____

_____  and  _____


_____         _____

_____  and  _____


_____         _____

_____  and  _____

Directions: Read each sentence. Put the quotation marks where they belong.

1. It's a nice day,  said Don.

   Let's walk on the beach.

2. That sounds like fun,  said Sheila.

   I'll get a bag for shells.

3. I don't see any shells,  said Don.

   Maybe we won't find any today.

4. Look over there,  said Sheila.

   There are lots of shells.

Directions: Read each sentence. Circle the quotation marks in each sentence. Draw a line under the exact words the person said.

1. "Let's help Grandpa," said Megan. "I think it would be fun."

2. "That is a good idea," said George. "We can feed the chickens."

3. "You find the grain," said Megan. "I will get the pails."

4. "I'll open this big sack," said George. "Then we can fill the pails."

5. "The chickens are clucking," said Megan. "They must be very hungry."

# Phonics

| goose | balloon | moon | flute | stew | moose |

_____

- - - - - - - - - - -

_____

_____

- - - - - - - - - - -

_____

## Writing Words

Directions: Look at the pictures and finish the sentences with the correct word.

_____

Karen _____ a picture.

| stew |
| drew |

_____

Tonya used _____ for her project.

| glue |
| drew |

## Dictation and Spelling

_____   _____

_____   _____

_____   _____

_____   _____

_____   _____

| I | we | they | she | it | you |

1. _____ walks slowly.

2. _____ bakes pies.

3. _____ can add.

4. _____ are going on a trip.

5. _____ need to feed the dog.

6. _____ read to each other.

**Pronouns**

Directions: Read the sentence. Draw a circle around the pronoun. On the line, write the word to which the pronoun refers. The first one is done for you.

1. Greg can spell.
   (He) is a good speller.

Greg

2. Sandy jogs.
   She runs every day.

3. Bill and Pete walk to the lake.
   They like to hike.

4. Jim, let's race.
   You like to run

5. The kitten plays a lot.
   It chases a toy mouse.

6. Dennis helps stack the wood.
   He is strong.

Directions: Draw a line between the two words that were put together to make the compound word. Write the two words on the lines

1. firewood

2. barnyard

3. lighthouse

4. sidewalk

5. upstairs

6. raincoat

7. blueberry

8. boxcar

*Compound Words* • **Reading and Writing Workbook**

## Grammar

Directions: Read the sentence. Circle each compound word. On the lines, write the two words that make the compound word.

1. Mike brings the game downstairs.

_____     _____

_____     _____

2. Please hand me the flashlight.

_____     _____

_____     _____

3. Joe put the books in the bookcase.

_____     _____

_____     _____

4. Craig put his letter in the mailbox.

_____     _____

_____     _____

5. Sarah likes blackberry jam.

_____     _____

_____     _____

Directions: On the top part of the page, copy the words and the sentence in the spaces provided. Then write rhyming words to finish the sentences on the bottom of the page.

# ow

## Writing Words and Sentences

how _____ now _____

Take a towel to the shower.

_____

- - - - - - - - - - - - - - - - - - - - - -

_____

- - - - - - - - - - - - - - - - - - - - - -

_____

A cow that was <u>brown</u> went to the _____ .

_____

The queen had a <u>crown</u> and a long green _____ .

# Word Study

Directions: Write the word described by each picture.

cat
cow
crow

_____

- - - - - - - - - - - - - - - -

_____

shower
tower
flower

_____

- - - - - - - - - - - - - - - -

_____

towel
owl
howl

_____

- - - - - - - - - - - - - - - -

_____

crown
gown
frown

_____

- - - - - - - - - - - - - - - -

_____

**End Punctuation**

1.  We are having a party _____

2.  Jason wants to put balloons everywhere _____

3.  Should I help him _____

4.  We blow up one balloon at a time _____

5.  A red balloon got away _____

6.  It's flying around the room _____

7.  Where did it land _____

8.  Let's put balloons on the door _____

9.  Do we need some by the window _____

10. The room looks colorful _____

**End Punctuation**

Our yard is full of yellow and red leaves ___

It looks so pretty ___ May Sarah and I rake the leaves___

We each rake a big pile of leaves ___ Now what do we

do with them ___ Sarah and I look at each other ___ We

stuff the leaves into big bags ___ Both of us are tired ___

Name _____

1. Christy tried to <u>jam</u> everything in the backpack.

    jelly       stuff

2. Flowers bloom in the <u>spring</u>.

    to leap       a season of the year

3. The bike is in the <u>shed</u>.

    a small building       to let fall off

4. Sheila made the boat <u>rock</u>.

    to move sideways       a stone

5. James <u>rose</u> late on Friday.

    flower       got up

6. Marv has a spinning <u>top</u>.

    highest place       toy

7. Let's have <u>rolls</u> with dinner.

    bread       tumbles

8. Claire used tape to <u>seal</u> the box.

    an animal       to close

**Vocabulary**

1. We can <u>park</u> our bikes near the <u>park</u>.

a green place
to put in a place

2. The clown had to <u>tie</u> his orange and red <u>tie</u>.

clothing worn at neck
to make a knot

3. <u>Can</u> Dave and Bill open the tin <u>can</u>?

container
to be able to

4. <u>Pop</u>, did you hear the balloon <u>pop</u>?

a short, loud sound
father

Name _____

## Sounds and Spellings

ow
ou_

## Writing Words and Sentences

out _____    house _____

A mouse ran out.

_____

_ _ _ _ _ _ _ _ _ _ _ _ _ _ _ _ _

_____

## Dictation and Spelling

_____    _____

_ _ _ _ _ _ _ _ _    _ _ _ _ _ _ _ _ _

_____    _____

_____    _____

_____    _____

_ _ _ _ _ _ _ _ _    _ _ _ _ _ _ _ _ _

**Vocabulary**

| how snow crow crown show |
|---|

_____

1. The queen has a _____ with a big round ruby.

2. Do you know _____ to play checkers?

3. The class put on a puppet _____.

4. The _____ made the ground white.

5. A _____ is a big black bird.

1. Jerry rode his bike to Mike's house _____

2. Look at that beautiful rainbow _____

3. When is Betsy going to visit _____

4. Our team won _____

5. The big bear growled at him _____

6. Who is going to walk the dog _____

7. A squirrel ran up and down the tree _____

8. Amy's puppy waits at the door for her _____

9. The fire bell suddenly rang _____

10. Where is the picnic _____

Name_____

1. Write a statement about the weather.

_____

- - - - - - - - - - - - - - - - - - - - -

_____

- - - - - - - - - - - - - - - - - - - - -

_____

2. Write a question about your teacher.

_____

- - - - - - - - - - - - - - - - - - - - -

_____

- - - - - - - - - - - - - - - - - - - - -

_____

3. Write an exclamation about your birthday.

_____

- - - - - - - - - - - - - - - - - - - - -

_____

- - - - - - - - - - - - - - - - - - - - -

_____

**Vocabulary**

| first | next | second | then |
|-------|------|--------|------|
| before | yesterday | after | last |

_____

1. Silvia will go home _____ week.

2. Bob reads a book _____ he goes to bed.

3. Becky is the _____ one in line behind Joe.

4. Carlos will read his story _____ Pat reads hers.

5. _____ it rained.

6. Anna wipes the dish and _____ puts it away.

7. David likes to be the _____ one on the bus.

8. We were the _____ to leave.

**Vocabulary**

1. After Pat cleans his room, he will go play.

2. Jane likes to be the first one out to recess.

3. We must go home before it gets dark.

4. Sam is the second person to read that book.

5. Betty played at my house yesterday.

6. Chuck will mow the grass and then water it.

7. Are we having pizza for dinner tonight?

8. Carol will be the next one to play a song.

9. They arrived later than everyone else.

10. Sherry is going to move tomorrow.

Directions: Write the word that goes with each picture.

| clown | round | owl | crowd | towel | hound |

_____

- - - - - - - - - - - - - -

_____

_____

- - - - - - - - - - - - - -

_____

_____

- - - - - - - - - - - - - -

_____

_____

- - - - - - - - - - - - - -

_____

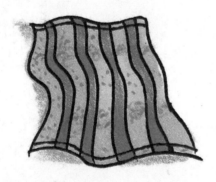

_____

- - - - - - - - - - - - - -

_____

_____

- - - - - - - - - - - - - -

_____

## Listening for Vowel Sounds

"What do you like about parades?" asked Mom.

"I like the sound of drums," said Byron, "but I wish they weren't so loud."

"The clowns are funny," added Suzy. "One of them was walking slow and made our dog growl."

"I like to see the crowd wave and clap," said Dad.

"I know what I like," said Mom. "I like to hear the bands beat their drums and toot their horns."

ou
_____

ow
_____

**Sounds and Spellings**

## aw
## au

**Writing Words and Sentences**

raw _____

bawl _____

pause _____

The baby crawls on the lawn.

_____

_____

_____

_____

*Vowel Sounds and Spellings* • **Reading and Writing Workbook**

## Sounds and Spellings

Directions: Look at the pictures and finish the sentences with the correct word.

_____

Paul poured milk in the _____.

| washer |
| saucer |

_____

The hawk raised its _____.

| straw |
| claw |

## Dictation and Spelling

_____    _____

_____    _____

_____    _____

_____    _____

_____    _____

Name _____

I am a <u>big</u> <u>gray</u> elephant.

Directions: Read the sentences. Draw a line under the adjectives.

1. A fluffy white kitten peeked out of the box.

2. Can we get new red notebooks for school?

3. Sally pulled the big warm quilt around her.

4. A large spotted dog sat by the gate.

5. Hal saw a bright yellow kite.

6. Devin walked up the steep rocky trail.

7. The clown wore a purple striped hat.

8. A mouse has a long skinny tail.

9. The machine made a loud clanking sound.

10. The old brown horse ate grass.

**Grammar**

| lacy | hard | new | big |
|------|------|------|------|
| new | old | weak | pretty |
| thick | thin | strong | wet |

_____ _____

1. Mark has a _____ _____ bike.

_____ _____

2. A newborn kitten has _____ _____ legs.

_____ _____

3. Sarah wore a _____ _____ dress.

_____ _____

4. A turtle has a _____ _____ shell.

_____ _____

5. Dan took off his _____ _____ shoes.

**Reading and Writing Workbook •** *Adjectives*

Tim crawls across the floor.
Tim pets the puppy.

He ate a piece of straw.
She wore a shawl.

A cow lies down.
A cow walked through town.

**Phonics**

how     cow     crawl     now

lawn     brown     town     crown

draw     down     saw     law

fawn     lawn     dawn     shawl

## Sounds and Spellings

Directions: Copy the words and the sentence on the lines.

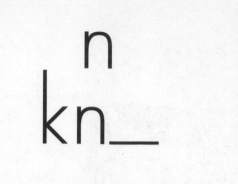

## Writing Words and Sentences

knit _____ knot _____

I know that knight.

_____

_____

_____

## Dictation and Spelling

_____  _____

_____  _____

_____  _____

_____

Directions: Write the word that best completes each sentence.

Name ______________________________

## Sounds and Spellings

**Unit 6 • Lesson 9**

know knock knight knee knot

1. Please ________________ on the door.

2. She learned how to tie a ________________.

3. Do you ________________ how to sew?

4. He hurt his ________________ playing football.

5. The ________________ married the princess.

**Grammar**

1. May 16 1984

2. April 7 1958

3. November 24 1998

4. February 13 1927

5. September 29 1972

6. October 5 1999

7. The date on the letter is March 2 1985.

8. On July 17 1999 we are going to Mexico.

9. Jennifer was born on January 24 1989.

10. Aunt Alexa will visit us on June 10 1999.

11. Our first state fair was on August 25 1932.

12. We moved to our new house on June 4 1994.

*Commas* • **Reading and Writing Workbook**

**Grammar**

1. Pendleton  Oregon

2. Richmond  Virginia

3. Honolulu  Hawaii

4. Lansing  Michigan

5. Seattle  Washington

6. Tucson  Arizona

7. Marsha moved to Dallas  Texas.

8. Patsy visited Lincoln  Nebraska.

9. Mike lives in Sacramento  California.

10. Rick wrote to Hal in Topeka  Kansas.

11. Grace was born near Miami  Florida.

12. Kevin goes fishing in Butte  Montana.

cookie    hook    boot    spoon    book    cook

_____

_____

_____

_____

_____

_____

**Phonics**

Directions: Look at the pictures and finish the sentences with the correct word.

wood
wool

_____

The sweater is made of _____.

shook
stood

_____

The wet puppy _____.

boot
book

_____

She read a _____.

1. Paul's car has a flat tire.

2. Bev's kitten is friendly.

3. John's puppy runs fast.

4. Maggie likes Susan's painting.

5. Where are Kevin's boots?

6. Cindy's throat is sore.

7. Who cleaned the rabbit's cage?

8. Bill filled the cat's dish.

*Possessive Nouns, Apostrophes* • **Reading and Writing Workbook**

1. Viv has this lunch.

2. A pig has a carrot.

3. Rose has this shop.

4. Peg has a horse.

5. The park has a slide.

Viv's lunch

___ sweeter

___ sweet

___ sweetest

___ highest

___ higher

___ high

___ cold

___ coldest

___ colder

___ harder

___ hard

___ hardest

**Vocabulary**

_____

The sun is _____ of all.

bright  brighter  brightest

_____

A pig has _____ legs than a sheep.

short  shorter  shortest

**Dictation and Spelling**

_____ _____

_____ _____

_____ _____

_____ _____

_____ _____

Name _____

**Sounds and Spellings**

oi

_oy

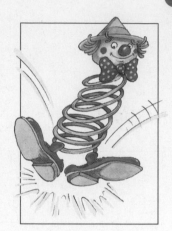

## Writing Words and Sentences

noise _____   joy _____

point _____   toy _____

The boy has a nice voice.

_____

_____

_____

*Vowel Sounds and Spellings* • **Reading and Writing Workbook**

## Phonics

Directions: Complete each sentence with the correct word.

| coins | toy | noise | moist | point |

_____

1. He got a _____ for his birthday.

_____

2. The pencil has a _____.

_____

3. She collects _____.

_____

4. The loud _____ woke us.

_____

5. The cake was soft and _____.

**Vocabulary**

Directions: Read the words. Write the correct contraction on the line.

| didn't | isn't | can't | doesn't |
|--------|-------|-------|---------|
| couldn't | hadn't | wasn't | aren't |

1. cannot

_____

2. are not

_____

3. does not

_____

4. did not

_____

5. could not

_____

6. is not

_____

7. was not

_____

8. had not

_____

*Contractions* • **Reading and Writing Workbook**

Vocabulary

Directions: Read each sentence. Circle the contraction that is formed by the underlined words in each sentence.

1. Jan <u>has not</u> made her lunch yet.　　haven't　hasn't

2. She and Pete <u>cannot</u> be late.　　can't　don't

3. "It <u>is not</u> too late," said Pete.　　wasn't　isn't

4. "We <u>do not</u> need to hurry,"
   said Jan.　　weren't　don't

5. Pete <u>had not</u> ever been late
   for school.　　hadn't　haven't

6. He <u>could not</u> wait for
   Jan any longer.　　wouldn't　couldn't

r

wr_

## Writing Words and Sentences

wrist

wrap

Robots wrestle rakes.

## Dictation and Spelling

*Consonant Sounds and Spellings* • **Reading and Writing Workbook**

## Sounds and Spellings

Directions: Write the word that goes with each picture.

| write | wrench | wreath | wrinkle |

_____
- - - - - - - - - - - - -
_____

_____
- - - - - - - - - - - - -
_____

_____
- - - - - - - - - - - - -
_____

_____
- - - - - - - - - - - - -
_____

**Reading and Writing Workbook •** *Blending*

1. man _____     mans     men

2. tooth _____     teeth     tooths

3. shelf _____     shelves     shelfs

4. mouse _____     mice     mouses

5. sheep _____     sheeps     sheep

6. goose _____     gooses     geese

7. moose _____     mooses     moose

8. ox _____     oxen     oxes

*Irregular Plurals* • **Reading and Writing Workbook**

_____

1. Mom bought two _____ of bread.

    loafs    loaves

_____

2. There are six _____ on each team.

    children    childs

_____

3. Ellie has three blue _____.

    scarves    scarf

_____

4. Three _____ helped us with our work.

    womans    women

_____

5. We watched four _____ swim in the pond.

    geese    gooses

## Sounds and Spellings

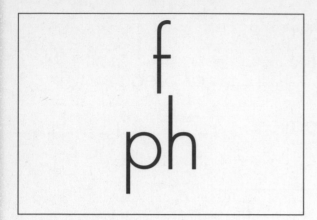

### Writing Words and Sentences

photo _____

phone _____

trophy _____

Phil's nephew plays the saxophone.

_____

_____

_____

Directions: Write the word that goes with each picture.

trophy   elephant   dolphin   gopher

_____

- - - - - - - - - - - - - - -

_____


_____

- - - - - - - - - - - - - - -

_____

_____

- - - - - - - - - - - - - - -

_____

_____

- - - - - - - - - - - - - - -

_____

Directions: Circle the time and order words. Then write the numbers 1, 2, 3, and 4 to tell the order the events happened.

___ Second, he put on his sneakers.

___ Finally, Jed ran to the gym.

___ First, Jed put on his uniform.

___ Then, he grabbed a basketball.

___ Then, she started to write.

___ First, Rosa sat at the desk.

___ Second, she got out paper and a pencil.

___ Finally, she finished her story.

**Vocabulary**

First   Second   Then   Finally

Directions: Read the sentences. Write the correct word to tell the order the events happened.

_____

_____, he found an acorn.

_____, the squirrel ran into the yard.

_____, he ran up a big branch.

_____

_____, Mabel took her hamster home.

_____, Mabel walked into the pet store.

_____, she looked at the animals.

Directions: Write the correct word to complete each sentence.

| phone | wrote | boil | elephant | wrap |

_____

1. I _____ Grandma a letter.

2. The water on the stove will _____.

3. Dad will _____ the gift.

4. The _____ rang.

5. We saw an _____ at the zoo.

## Phonics

1. wrap   wreath   rake   wrist

2. phone   photo   farm   elephant

3. foam   boil   soil   foil

4. voice   noise   tube   point

5. boy   bed   toy   joy

## Dictation and Spelling

_____    _____

- - - - - - - - - - - - -    - - - - - - - - - - - - -

_____    _____

_____    _____

- - - - - - - - - - - - -    - - - - - - - - - - - - -

_____    _____

_____    _____

- - - - - - - - - - - - -    - - - - - - - - - - - - -

_____    _____